Tomi's Time

Tomi's Time

In Love and Loss—and Rebirth from Bacterial Meningitis

Tom Zarzaca

BOOKLOGIX®

BOOKLOGIX®
Alpharetta, GA

The medical accounts contained in this book are those of a single individual from the perspective of his immediate family. These accounts are not intended to convey specific medical advice to any other individual, and they are not intended to provide recommendation for or against any specific choice in medical care.

10 9 8 7 6 5 4 3 2   0 5 1 9 1 4

Printed in the United States of America

ISBN: 978-1-61005-471-3

♾ This paper meets the requirements of ANSI/NISO Z39.48-1992 (Permanence of Paper)

This book is dedicated to Tomi and others like him whose Pure Light draws us from the shadows.

Last of he will be able to see the sun, and not mere reflections of him in the water, but he will see him in his own proper place, and not in another; and he will contemplate him as he is.

Plato
The Republic, Book VII, 360 BCE

Translated by
Benjamin Jowett

Contents

Acknowledgments

It's *all* about Mommy and the salvation she delivers to father and son, alike!

Prologue

T he story that follows is told of and for our son, Tomi, who is a survivor of bacterial meningitis. We tell Tomi's story to draw attention to his silence. We hold up our son and his unique experience to illuminate things unseen in darkness and shadow. And we offer a certain perspective on family recovery and moving forward in the hope of giving voice to Tomi and families like ours, after the unthinkable happens to their child.

The following passage opens doors in Tomi's time for you, family and friends, parents, and others who can lend understanding and time for his story of love, loss, and rebirth. We started writing this passage during Tomi's initial recovery from meningitis and our gradual awakening to the joy that our son would live. Yet at that time, we couldn't have fathomed the realities of raising Tomi with profound hearing and vision loss, severe seizure disorder, motor function impairment, and a host of other medical problems that are deeply rooted in his damaged brain. Now with this perspective, we look back to this passage and its then-untested hope to remember the best and worst parts of Tomi's time—for they both impact the present, and in their own unique ways, they strengthen and guide us through an uncertain future.

~Our son,

On this day of your birth, the morning sun brightens the sky, and a gentle breeze stirs with the promise of great change and unimaginable love. May 29, 2009~

The change that followed this day has brought celebration of Tomi's life full circle, beginning with the joy of birth and wonder of endless possibilities and carrying through nine months of pure delight as his personality developed and spirit grew.

But that was just the first part of Tomi's time, and it was a celebration of a certain kind—the usual kind, in which a child grows strong in love and devotion, where the pleasure of sacrifice opens the world to him, and where the celebration, itself, can obscure any number of other realities.

What followed that time was an end to all things perfect and the beginning of Tomi's life after surviving bacterial meningitis. During his most critical weeks, life and death each claimed their shares, as his body fought the infection but lost out to time and to a litter of strokes that would ultimately define his life. At that time, silent darkness was everything—and all things—but that was *only* just the beginning...

And this beginning for Tomi—in all its different forms, with all its different meanings, and for all the change it brings—draws us from near and far around this child to rejoice at his return to life, to hope for possibilities, and to delight in progress like never before. Now, the celebration of Tomi's time is of a different kind, but in some ways, it's the same—when an end meets new life and unimaginable love finds its way.

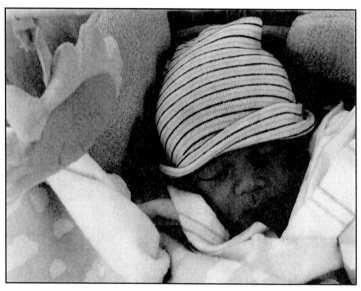

Sunrise at Four Days

Nine Months of
Pure Delight

Nine months of pure delight began for Yuko and me with a rising sun and gentle breeze and letters of promise to our son-to-be that he would one day know our love. We wrote to him that morning about the great change we expected to come, beginning just hours from then, but we had no previous experience or real perspective to gauge the magnitude of its coming. We told him of our plans and hopes for the future and pledged our devotion to his happiness and well-being as he made his way through life. We tried to express to him our imagined love with humble, few words and full expectation the rest would come to us in time. And with that, we put away the letter for later reading—and later writing, when the time *would* come—and we packed our things for the road and headed to the hospital to deliver our new life.

What's in a Name

Even though things were a little complicated by a nuchal cord issue and an elective cesarean section, Tomi's delivery couldn't have gone better and our joy no greater, if not for being stuck in a nameless quandary until the day of Yuko's discharge. We remember that first night and following couple days in the hospital room, face-to-face with a most extraordinary little creature who was just as beautiful to us as he was still unknown; so we only wanted a longer look and a little more time to give a name to his face. Our list of names was long though, maybe twice as long as some, with ones in English and others in Japanese in honor of Yuko's heritage. But time was so short, and the hospital staff was already thinking *John Doe* so the discharge paperwork could be processed.

We wanted him to have a Japanese name but struggled with one that had just the right meaning. All the while, others kept talking about how kids in school might react to an unusual name. They also seemed to have their own idea about a name but maybe no one *less* vocal about it (and more to the point) than Dad—born Vincenzo Zarzaca, given the middle name of Thomas for Confirmation, and later going by Vincent Thomas. When my turn came, I received a name in the same as Dad's junior but was called

Tommy to differentiate the two of us. Then in that twenty-fourth hour, when pinned between indecision, the hospital's vote for "John," and the humble wishes of a great old man, our son would become the third in line to carry our name forward.

There still was a practical matter to resolve, though. The problem was that my familiar name was already taken; so we couldn't just call him Tommy or Tom. Doing so would have invited unnecessary confusion among family and friends, and variations of our first name seemed far too serious for a baby. Besides, that name was taken, too. But with a stroke of beautiful simplicity and natural grace, Yuko began writing "Tomi" on the calendar to schedule his baby business, and she gave voice to his name, as spoken in Japan with familiar affection—*Tomi-chan.*

We have sung this name to him every day since, sometimes in whispered breath upon his cheek and other times in a cacophony of musical love that can only be expressed at the top of our lungs. Whether the song's meaning reaches him better by whisper or shout remains to be seen, but to the Japanese—and for Yuko and me—*Enrich* is the meaning in Tomi's name either way we sing it.

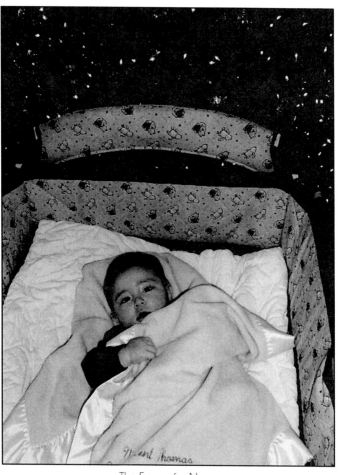

The Face of a Name

A Celebration of the Usual Kind

Our celebration of Tomi's time through those first six months might be shared by any number of new parents, filled by the joy of new life and absolutely amazed at the miracle of their baby's growth. However, any parent knows the first several months isn't *all* joy and wonder of endless possibilities. The fact is a certain amount of parent-building necessarily accompanies the bliss. For us, it was a whole different set of routines to get used to—figuring out personal care and handling requirements so as not to cause any damage; being tied to the feeding cycle and its sleepless return; handling the checkups, immunizations, and other baby business; continuing on with careers despite having something much more valuable at home; having to depend on daycare *because* of our careers; then treating the bugs that accompanied daycare and Tomi as they found their way home. But all these things paled in the light of Tomi's new life—a light that seemed to leave no shadows behind but only celebration and great joy for our new blessing.

Over the following three months or so, Tomi began tuning in and interacting in ways not possible in those first several months of life. In the beginning, the change wasn't quite noticeable, but later, it seemed like every day brought a heightened sense of awareness or some different skill we hadn't seen in him before. At first, it was all about the sound—coming from everywhere yet nowhere at times, still unintelligible but some of it familiar and comforting from previous experience; then there was the common experience of diaper time and Chopin's Nocturne No. 2, whose melodious ebb and flow may have spoken volumes of Tomi's time to come without us having to say a single word to him; and other times, the sound was our own song of enrichment that sang of the present and dreamt of our future together.

We also remember those bright eyes, crystal clear and clearly focused—at first on things in immediate range: a little face staring back at himself in the mirror with amused fascination, our faces there too, reflecting the joy of parenthood and the familiar source of those comforting sounds. Then later, eyes locking onto a prize and some added sense of what a couple hands can do: A quick grab of the cell phone, still unaware of its utility and undersized for the task but driven to explore and possess and even take a taste or two. Other times, the prize was a little kitty tail, perfectly sized, warm and fuzzy, with a twitch...then another grab and hold for dear life, with no questions of usefulness or ownership, only fascinated determination and bits of fur from its former owner, who answers around our home (and in Japan) to Neko.

And toward the end, all Tomi's senses began growing together to produce a perfect little child whose world was just then opening: sitting and balancing; hopping about in the bouncy with a face full of smiles and giggles; that little mouth flying open to snatch a spoonful of pureed sweet potatoes or working a yummy handful of snack cracker on his own. A happy child, seldom crying or fussing, with an emerging personality that was a little bit on the serious or thoughtful side, working things out in his head and just beginning to make sense of the life around him. Then *right* there at the end, maybe the fondest and most enduring memory of all: arriving at daycare in the afternoon, the sound of our voices carrying the din, then recognition and a quick turn and huge smile—borne of a bond with Tomi that began nine months earlier and that promised to be continued just down the road. For then, it was time for us to go home.

All light produces a shadow, however, depending on perspective—even the light of a child's new life and his emergence into an unfolding world. When cast against the dark backdrop of an ill-fated decision (a premature move to a new house in the wrong location, a lesser choice for career and daycare, a mistaken turn at a critical crossroad), the shadow can disappear, as can the notion of any other possible realities. It isn't until the road begins to turn that the shadow first comes into view, but by then, only perspective and time would reveal its full magnitude.

Companion for the Road

Prelude to an Uncertain Future

Thursday, March 4, 2010—There was a cell phone ring from Tomi's daycare center and a report that he was sick with a high fever and needed to be picked up early. By the time I got there that afternoon, Tomi's fever had gone back down, but he was noticeably ill. And faced with the two options of either taking him to his pediatrician for a late afternoon sick appointment or going home to care for him ourselves, I made that first decision that changed the course of the road we're on.

Three minutes later, we were back home and well into Tomi's sick business, waiting for Yuko to get home from work and proceeding with the usual afternoon routines. With our perspective at that point, taking Tomi home seemed to be the thing to do. That morning, he didn't appear sick; his fever was down, and we were fully equipped at home to care for him ourselves. So, this is just what we did.

Friday, March 5, Yuko stayed home to take care of Tomi, and I went to work as usual. Serious concern started growing over the course of the day as his fever went up to 102°F, then down and up again, until it finally peaked at 104°F that afternoon. By then, I had returned from work, but Tomi's pediatrician had already closed. So after talking to the pediatrician's answering service, the attendant had an on-call nurse from a local children's hospital call us back to get a report on Tomi's condition and to advise us on what we should do for him.

During that phone conversation, I discussed Tomi's fever pattern over the preceding thirty hours, his decreased appetite and increased sleeping, the loss of his smile...but for a nine-month-old baby, these conditions might have been expected from any number of bugs that kids can catch. And looking back with current knowledge, we now understand some of the questions that nurse asked: if he was un-wakable when asleep, if he exhibited certain neurological symptoms when awake, if there had been any projectile vomiting. However, none of these conditions were the case at that point. So, we concluded the conversation with questions of what to look for over the weekend and at what point would it become necessary to go to an emergency room. *What's the fever limit? How do we know when it's time?* Her response, "Watch for symptom changes"—that it's more about major changes in symptoms than a certain degree of fever, particularly for the kinds of symptoms she had just asked about. So with this knowledge and a feeling of having just received good advice, the consultation ended, and Yuko and I carried on as usual, until an early bedtime came for all of us that evening.

Early Saturday morning, I was up to find Tomi awake and burning hot. He was horribly sick, and it was a mad rush to get him downstairs, checked out, and to figure out what to do. First thing, I tried wiping his face with a cool rag...*but the screaming!* Then I got a little formula in him and gave him a dose of children's pain medicine...still the crying and screaming, followed by a shot of vomit that emptied the contents of his entire stomach! Then another attempt at feeding and a half-dose of medicine, both of which were rejected in a second blast. Yuko was up at that point, and it was clear symptoms had changed. We then collected whatever was necessary for the trip, and we were out the door in a flash, plotting a course for the closest children's hospital.

We knew a children's hospital was the place to take Tomi. So at 7:15 in the morning, we sped from our driveway with one in mind. But the road that would ultimately take us there never dawned on us, and terrible worry for Tomi's condition called to question the forty-five-minute drive ahead. Then came a crossroad along the way and another decision, made in a split second. Three minutes later, we were rushing Tomi into the emergency room of our local county hospital, desperate to get emergency care for him and hoping it didn't matter where.

With our understanding of things now, a critical twenty-four-hour window for Tomi's type of meningitis had already opened. But we didn't know. The hospital staff didn't know. And the ER doctor on contract that morning didn't know—not that a permanent, real-time doctor at a children's hospital would have—not that parents with such limited perspective could have. We all should have known though: Tomi's high fever over the preceding couple days, the projectile vomiting that followed, his lethargy as he slept through this first ER visit and beyond, the diagnosed ear infection, the obvious infection that had begun running from his eyes.

But with prescriptions for his ear and eye infections and one for nausea, Tomi was discharged from the ER with an assumed hodgepodge of minor ailments, when in fact, it was a bug that would destroy nearly everything. No test was done to rule out this bug, and the antibiotic necessary for stopping it was never given; no urinalysis done; no bloodwork was collected, much less a simple throat swab to check for infection, and there was no discussion on admitting Tomi for observation or even referring him to a children's hospital just to be sure. Instead, we were discharged from the emergency room in less than two hours with three prescriptions and a false sense of satisfaction and well-being.

And it's one of our bitter ironies—perhaps the first, if not the worst—passing by that crossroad as we made our way back home that morning, a little self-congratulatory for having changed course and gotten immediate care for Tomi, feeling satisfied things would be okay, and unaware of what would come in less than twenty-four hours…

We woke to predawn screaming Sunday morning, the likes of which we had never heard before but a mere prelude to future events. Looking back with current understanding, it's clear that nothing had been okay. All the sleeping Tomi did since the ER visit the day before wasn't rest and healing; it was deepening lethargy from the ongoing attack on his central nervous system. His low-grade fever, which persisted during that same period, couldn't be broken. And that diagnosed ear infection, which turned out to be raging in both ears, was maybe one reason for the screaming that woke us that morning—not to mention what a stroke might feel like. By that time too, Tomi looked curiously different than a baby that just happened to be very sick. We didn't catch it at first, but it was that slight bit of swelling and that shade of lifelessness that comes on as blood goes septic. And even though we couldn't quite put it all together then, that look on Tomi's face and those ear-piercing screams weren't right, and it was another mad rush to get him emergency care as fast as possible.

We returned to the emergency room at our county hospital, for there seemingly was no time to drive anywhere else. That same doctor was there. He remembered us from the morning before. The baby was somehow different though. But after almost two hours into Tomi's re-admission, the ER doctor finally realized the consequences of the previous day's decisions. At that point, he notified Children's Healthcare of Atlanta, and they began coordinating Tomi's care remotely from the Pediatric Intensive Care Unit at Scottish Rite Hospital.

They knew what it was by then, even without meningitis test results. The Children's ICU team was already acting on it and in direct communication with the ER doctor. Vancomycin was needed to stop the infection and had been all along. So the hospital staff tried getting an IV started to deliver the antibiotic directly to Tomi's bloodstream, but they couldn't hit a vein...then another failed attempt...and possibly a third. It was Tomi's chubby little arms and that slight bit of swelling that made it so difficult. At that point, the Children's paramedic ground crew arrived and only needed a quick look and a few vital signs to determine that a second life-flight paramedic crew would be needed. The first crew then began administering emergency care for

Tomi, and out went the lights! A vein in his arm was backlit with a flashlight in a move that was utterly brilliant, and the paramedics hit it without pause or error. Then, the antibiotic that would ultimately save Tomi's life started flowing.

The first of ten thousand seizures had already occurred earlier during this second ER visit, before the paramedic ground crew ever arrived. This was, in all likelihood, the event that spurred the ER doctor to call the Children's team in the first place. At that point, the hospital staff inserted an endotracheal tube into Tomi's airway and started him on a ventilator to assist his breathing. However, nearly thirty minutes passed after Tomi's initial intubation before it was realized that his endotracheal tube was misplaced, with its tip located in "an apparent blockage of the left mainstem bronchus, and the left lung now (then) being airless." As a result, Tomi suffered from acute respiratory failure with decreased oxygen to his brain—which was already under attack from the pneumococcal infection. After the life-flight paramedic crew arrived and the misplacement was discovered, both crews labored to correct the intubation of Tomi's airway and restore oxygen to his brain.

Then came the life-flight to Scottish Rite, an end to nine months of pure delight, and silent darkness that will last Tomi's entire life.

Life after Surviving Bacterial Meningitis

At First

For parents who are now suffering with your baby, fighting for life and facing the prospect of losing everything, this is for you.

We felt your desperation, as all news about your child's condition progressively worsens and when coming to the realization that none of the potential outcomes will be good ones. We remember that feeling of helplessness as our baby lay lifeless, and we recall a horror that followed a deafening awakening into pain and screaming. We know that feeling of being alone and of time ceasing, as life blasts by with cruel disregard for life lost. We feel the regret for decisions made—and decisions un-made—and we know the fear of the road down which those decisions will ultimately lead.

We've been down, and still follow, this road which may not be very different than the one that lays before you...

> *Now, more than ever, it's important to know that not all outcomes will be bad ones. Some can even be amazingly beautiful.*

> *And that pain of loss and that terror that now devours everything is about as bad as it can ever get. So, don't let go! Keep talking to your baby, and this worst bit will pass.*

> *And you will find that you're not alone and it's only "Life" that's happening—nothing more. Life does go on, and it can do so in the manner you choose and the time you keep.*

> *And those decisions that may have regrettably led to this moment in time...they're not bad ones to forever be questioned and lamented. They were simply decisions that inexorably led us to the place we are always supposed to be—which is simply the road just underfoot.*

Even as similarly as our roads may have started and as common as some of the outcomes may be, our journeys will diverge in their own unique ways. All people are individuals; all parents come to their children in their own special ways, and no child whose brain is damaged due to meningitis—or otherwise—is, or ever will be, the same. However, this is neither the end of the story nor the sum of all things. And even though it doesn't feel that way right now, what just happened is only just the beginning.

What Just Happened to Our Baby

Meningitis in General—

Authorities generally categorize the five types of meningitis as bacterial, viral, parasitic, fungal, and non-infectious. Each of these types ranges in overall severity, which also depends on how early treatment begins. However, all types commonly result in inflammation of the meninges—or the protective membranes of the brain and/or spinal cord. For the infectious types of meningitis, the general nature and the location within the central nervous system where the inflammation occurs depends on the specific kind of infection. Furthermore, this agent-specific response produces unique medical outcomes if the infection is allowed to progress.

Strep-Pneumococcal Meningitis—

Bacterial meningitis, particularly Tomi's type caused by Streptococcus pneumoniae, is considered one of the most dangerous forms of meningitis given its ability to cause severe brain damage and death within a very short period of time. Untreated pneumococcal meningitis can run its course in twenty-four hours, at which point, there is little-to-no hope for a return to normal life—if life, at all, happens to find a way.

However, pneumococcal meningitis doesn't just begin as such, and it's not a contagious infection, as say the flu is or some other kinds of bacterial infections. Tomi's type of meningitis, instead, follows from a typical strep infection in the nose or throat, which is readily transmitted through coughing or sneezing. This type of bug and its mode of transmission are fairly common in group environments such as schools, daycares, malls, etc., but once established in its host, the infection can usually be overcome by the body's immune system and some help from antibiotics. The leap from typical strep infection to meningitis occurs if the germ is able to cross the blood-brain barrier, which is far less common than the original infection itself. However, once the infection establishes itself on the other side, it becomes a simple matter of time unless it is diagnosed and aggressively treated with strong antibiotics.

The severity of the illness begins with the inflammatory response within the brain, which restricts or stops internal blood flow. This then leads to centralized areas of brain cell death—or "strokes" in common terms. Depending on where in the brain the strokes occur, various bodily systems can be impacted as the brain's control of those systems is compromised or outright destroyed. For the most extreme cases of infection, the inner walls that surround the ventricles (or fluid-filled spaces) in the brain are destroyed by the bacteria, impacting the brain's ability to absorb the fluid and control internal pressure. Damage or shutdown of other organs can also accompany the brain damage in the worst cases. This generally results from septicemia, or blood poisoning, that is caused by the overwhelming presence of bacteria and its toxins in the circulating blood.

Some of the potential outcomes of untreated pneumococcal meningitis include deafness (sensorineural hearing loss), blindness (cortical vision impairment), spatial disorientation, seizure disorder, hydrocephalus (fluid build-up and pressure in the brain), problems with cognition and behavior, and motor function impairment. However, while this listing is in no way all-inclusive, not all pneumococcal meningitis cases produce all of these results. The infection is detectable, and when diagnosed early, it can be stopped by strong antibiotics and with minimal long-term effects.

In Tomi's case, the infection did run its full course, leading him to a point where there was little distinction between life and death. As life eventually prevailed for him, however, all of the above outcomes have resulted to a profound degree—each of which are debilitating and permanent in themselves, but combined, produce a wholly different kind of disability that's far greater than the sum of its parts.

The best way to prevent this unthinkable outcome is to keep current on immunizations—particularly for young children, the elderly, and people with compromised immune systems. For pneumococcal meningitis in particular, pay attention to infections of the ears, nose, and throat, and watch for symptoms of very high fever, lethargy, and other neurological symptoms like projectile vomiting and sometimes a stiffened neck. When it's clear from these symptoms that emergency care is needed, choose the best available hospital, and don't hesitate getting a second opinion if any questions remain.

Tomi's Recovery to Start

For those who survive such an end, it's difficult to define a point in time that death first yields to life, and recovery from advanced bacterial meningitis begins. In the broadest sense, Tomi's recovery began after the Children's paramedics arrived on scene and started treating the infection. But over the course of his following two-month hospitalization, setbacks, re-emergencies, and additional surgeries and procedures blurred any distinction between recovery and decline. And this carries through the present time, albeit with abated frequency and intensity, but with ongoing regularity and urgency, nonetheless.

So with this perspective, we've come to understand that recovery from Tomi's kind of meningitis is something completely different than a marked one-time event, after which medical problems are overcome and even condition-appropriate milestones are likely reached. Instead, recovery of Tomi's kind continues life-long. It's ever-changing, but in many ways, very little changes at all. And for those that love and care for a child recovering in this way, the pain and hardship that must gratefully be embraced beg for its own kind of healing and recovery.

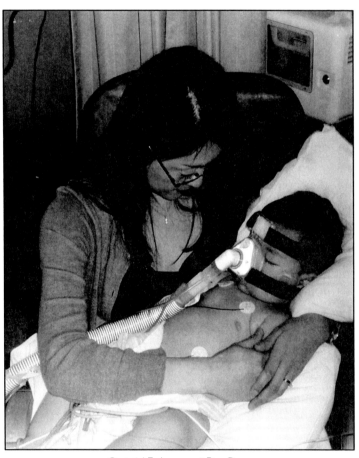

Grateful Embrace at Five Days

Flashes in Time—

We owe Tomi's recovery to the heroic actions of the Scottish Rite doctors, nurses, paramedics, specialists, and therapists who fought for his life, and who through love of profession, exemplify the highest standards in medical care for children. We remain humbled and will always be grateful to everyone who laid their loving, healing hands on our son and for the compassion and care that we too received as we came to realize that Tomi would never be the same.

Since being admitted to Scottish Rite that first time, Tomi's recovery has teetered along a continuum, bounded between the limits of coma-borne lifelessness and his present existence as young boy whose animations are little more advanced than those of a newborn baby.

Therefore in one sense, there isn't a lot of ground to cover between where Tomi started and where he is now—an irony that's honed by the fact that some aspects of his recovery are permanently marked by backward progress. But it's not possible to describe Tomi's "short" journey in recovery with narrative detail because so much has happened, both seen and unseen, and because it can't ever be complete, anyway, without Tomi telling it himself.

So the following flashes in time simply recount some of the main events of Tomi's recovery, as branded through mind and soul and, where possible, as imagined from Tomi's perspective.

Day 1—

Scottish Rite Pediatric Intensive Care Unit, first ten seconds—Shock and paralysis! Blasted by pain and loss, and some distant, fading sound: "Nothing about your baby is okay." Then again, "Nothing about his condition is normal."

Day 2 and Beyond—

Tomi swollen-taut, deathly white, still, and silent...*Our baby doesn't look like this! Dear God this can't be him—* all the penetrating tubes and wires, the humming machines, and blaring alarms...*No! Please don't let this happen*—as the medical team moved about with urgent determination.

And that first neurologist, then showing a Magnetic Resonance Image (MRI) of Tomi's brain which was lit up with strokes, top-to-bottom, inside-to-out—in a view eerily mindful of stars and galaxies in space and utter loss in the darkness between. The only advice he gave:

"Keep talking to your baby"—a strangely ironic suggestion in light of the blazing galaxies in Tomi's temporal lobes but *the* best personal advice any of his doctors ever gave us.

Then it was a problem of septicemia and poisoned blood and the likely culprit of that swelling that rendered things unrecognizable. A blood transfusion was immediately needed, and American Red Cross was already en route (*along a road we traveled most every day, perhaps by a driver, previously passed along the way*). At that point though, an ICU doctor was talking about bloodwork results: something to do with kidneys and liver and abnormal levels...*No! Please wait!*

And along came an ophthalmologist with an amazing collection of lenses, tools, and devices. But none were needed to see Tomi's eyes randomly drifting about, sometimes fluttering with supernatural speed, pupils unresponsive. For the question of vision had just been answered in the heavens. Instead, the subject was Tomi's optic nerves and whether or not they were bulging under the force of intracranial pressure. No abnormalities to speak of, and his optic nerves were, then, still pink with life.

Still and silent, "without form, and void, and darkness upon the face of the deep": a Genesis of sorts—a drug-induced coma which seemingly began ages before. But unlike any sort of big bang, Tomi's emergence began with the medical team slowly discontinuing the drug to lift the coma. It didn't just end though. There was no grand awakening or even a coming-to-being, and no one would say why. Instead, Tomi emerged by imperceptible degrees and through a slow progression of little twitches and jerks—at first, in response to unpleasant stimuli and only on his right side—and later, sporadic, unprovoked movements and even a twitching toe on his weak side. All the while, Tomi remained silenced by an endotracheal tube that continued breathing life into him from a ventilator. But some incoherent, muted sound was welling up from the deep and crying for release. Then was not quite the time though, but it surely would come...

Weeks and Months Beyond—

With the infection terminated, fresh blood, and some semblance of his former self, it was time to take Tomi off the ventilator to see if he could protect his airway and maintain oxygen levels. He had been intubated with that tube in his airway since the first day, but the only way to know if he would breathe normally was to pull it, force the challenge on him, and wait for the response…"We need you to leave the room now; we'll call you when we're done" (in what became some sort of ritual in endotracheal tube handling, with visions of shamans and snakes hovering over our gagging, choking baby)…But afterwards, *the* most beautiful sight: Tomi tube-free and breathing on his own—but not strongly. He aspirated secretions, and his oxygen levels weren't quite right, but the Children's team had ways of handling that. Then, that muted sound lightly broke the surface in an emergent musical of cries and feeble screams that brought joy and thankfulness like never before imagined!

But Tomi's tune changed. Almost without notice and in a matter of no time came a deafening awakening into pain and screaming that was all the more unthinkable. Some might have witnessed Tomi's wailing agony, his rigid contractures, and that convulsing little form and seen a baby being devoured by the devil. All we kept wondering was if God would save something for us. However, a CT scan showing the structure of Tomi's brain revealed a simpler explanation: abnormally large ventricles, intracranial pressure, and his brain crammed against the inside of his skull. For Tomi, the name of the offender meant nothing, and this time, no ophthalmologist was needed to see the hell pouring forth from his head. This time, a neurosurgeon was on tap to place a temporary catheter deep inside Tomi's brain to drain the fluid and relieve the pressure—and after that, a second surgery to internalize the shunt from head to abdomen. When it was all over, all we could do was surrender our baby to something better. And on the Easter Sunday that followed, Tomi was baptized by an old family friend and teacher, and we gave silent, humbled thanks for what little bit remained.

Sometime earlier during Tomi's time in ICU, there was a hearing test with negative results that confirmed the images in his MRI. But typical and presumed fluid buildup in his inners ears could have affected those results. So minor surgery was needed to place a couple ear tubes, get the fluid drained, and then perform a second Auditory Brainstem Response test. But this hearing test, unlike others, required general anesthesia which required the ventilator and re-intubation of Tomi's airway, which meant the tube handlers had to get involved yet again—before and after the test. In spite of that, the results in both ears: 500 Hz–4,000 Hz, 90 dB, No Response..."abnormal conduction of the auditory pathway through the level of the brainstem bilaterally consistent with severe to profound sensori-neural hearing loss." Grandfather, father, and son all present at the end of a line to receive the audiologist's news which had already descended upon each of us in its own unique ways.

A month into his hospitalization, Tomi transitioned to the rehab unit, and it was time to get him off of IV feedings, which couldn't continue forever. But motor centers in his brain were lit up too. What's more, no MRI was needed to see Tomi's motor function problems—the involuntary jerks and spasms, his disconnectedness with his hands, the inability for him to hold his head up or even swallow normally (so said several swallowing studies). Then came a feeding pump and the powdered formula and another tube procedure, but this one was a tummy tube (or G-tube) to deliver nutrition straight to his stomach (setting aside the question of whether or not things would work from stomach to bottom). Things did work though in spite of the failed spoon feedings, trials and errors in various formulas, acquired food allergies, the gagging and vomiting, replacement of his G-tube, placement of a G-J tube to also feed into his jejunum, multiple replacements of that device, and so forth—all zero-sum prices to keep Tomi sustained. But those pureed sweet potatoes sure were a hit in some distant past, as was the sight of that little mouth flying open in anticipation of a rich spoonful.

Loss of senses unheard of: So it likely went for Tomi's vestibular and proprioceptive senses, which are generally responsible for awareness and orientation of the body's position and movement in the surrounding environment. We've heard these senses are typically damaged by Tomi's type of meningitis, and we recall the neurologist saying something about these regions of space as well. We also remember Tomi's time in rehab and beyond, when a touch would make him flinch and cry out and when he screamed every time he was moved—not to mention therapy horror. Tomi's inability to balance his head or sit unassisted, to use his arms or legs for leverage, or to roll over are all probable manifestations of these damaged senses as well. And Tomi's hearing and vision loss make his orientation problems all the worse because he can't witness the world beyond his reach. Tomi is also completely passive to the forces around him, and he's not only disconnected from this external environment, but there's also a disconnect with his own body. But he *has* figured out how to nibble on his right forefinger (or his YumYum, as we think of it)— but *never* that other one. And he now can be calmed by love and tender touch, wrapped in embrace and face-to-face. If only he could remember this love and reach out for it when we're gone, then our privileged business as parents would be about as complete as it could ever be.

Then, Tomi's tone changed again, from his typical cries and screams of being touched and rehabilitated to something wholly different. But this time, the horror was deafeningly familiar. This time, the shunt that had been placed to moderate Tomi's brain pressure was clogged, and emergency surgery was again necessary. And with the devil's return, it seemed that conversations with God were either useless or they were somehow working against him. It doesn't matter either way when a baby's in hell, and all that can be done is join him there until it ends.

Then it was a problem with Tomi's breathing while he slept. In deep sleep, his respiration rates would decrease to the point where his blood oxygen levels would plunge. In the real world, it was a bad case of sleep apnea. But for Tomi—and his problem with aspirating secretions, his impaired motor function, and lingering questions about all the stars in space—it seemingly was a matter of life or death. But this problem had a common solution called a pulse oximeter, a device that detects blood oxygen levels and issues an alarm when they drop below a preset minimum. Then it was a matter of rousing Tomi awake and getting his respirations back up. Tomi's pulse-ox also provided unexpected sleep and cardiovascular therapy: Deeply sleeping, daring to dream...Then that JOLT from its blaring report and a nightmare of little blue lips! Heart rate from 60 to 160 in no time, and from bed to crib and on top of baby in a single horizontal motion! Thankfully, Tomi recovered beyond the need for his pulse-ox along the way. We too grew a little stronger with its use, and despite this (or maybe because of it), we still find times when it's okay to dream.

Seizures every day, all the time, and no end in sight: Some seven thousand or more in that first two and a half years—simply using an average of eight per day, but in later times, more like ten or fifteen each day and lasting anytime between several seconds and fifteen minutes. Tomi's kinds of seizures are just as varied. Multiple kinds can occur at once, and they are always changing: Tomi has suffered jerky seizures, rigid seizures, drop seizures, absence seizures, and vocalizing seizures—which, in themselves, include a variety of expressions of human emotion like humor, happiness, delight, and sadness, surprise, and fright. And all this despite multiple combinations of seizure meds of various type: At first Keppra and Clonazepam, then discontinue Keppra and start Topiramate, and use Diastat in emergency for ones lasting longer than five minutes—then longer than fifteen minutes—but that combo wasn't right; so discontinue Topiramate and try Trileptal, to no effect, but discontinue that one too because it *can* affect electrolytes; then add Banzel, and try Depakene which can cause liver damage so include Levocarnitine for that, but that combo wasn't right; so go back to Keppra, Clonazepam, and Banzel, and use Diastat as needed; still, ten to twenty-five per day, excluding night; so start the Ketocal diet (twice), stop the Banzel, and start taking Clobazam as well. So it remains a desperate plight as nothing about it is cut and dry, when it's only a pale shade of gray in between and a pillshot blast into finite space.

But all that says nothing about Tomi's seizure reality: What he experiences when his head and limbs snap into sudden contracture or when his whole body falls limp under gravity's enduring command...What's happening in his head when his eyes roll to the back of it, as if all the stars and galaxies are racing into sharp focus...What he feels when his funny bone is tickled or when that sweet smile sweeps across his face...What comes over him when those little lips pucker in seeming disappointment or when he cries out as if the devil has returned. And it's another one of those pointed ironies that these expressions of human emotion remain deeply rooted in Tomi's damaged brain despite all the loss but that, because of it, he only really expresses them when he's actively seizing.

Setting aside the seizures (and the vomiting, which is a whole other issue depending on whether it's head or gut related), Tomi grew more medically stable, and he was able to stay well enough at home—save a dozen or more ER visits, additional hospitalizations, and other special procedures since that first stay. So we opted for another surgery to place a cochlear implant into Tomi's right inner ear to try and make some connection with him through sound. He had previously tried hearing aids to no effect, but unlike those, this implant would conduct sound directly into his brain (setting aside the question of what his brain would do with the sound when it got there). Other than that, direct physical contact was all we had to reach Tomi, which is, itself, problematic given his propensity to cry out or scream when being touched or handled. So, after about three and a half hours into a surgery that typically lasts only a couple or so, the nurse came out to inform that things were okay but that a problem had developed during the surgery. Apparently, Tomi was highly allergic to the morphine they gave him for pain, and the anaphylactic shock that ensued caused the delay—but the implant was in, and they were just wrapping up. So she suggested we go up to the room and wait on him there...And so it goes for Tomi's delicate condition, where even the simplest things aren't easy and where a stable condition can turn at any moment—

almost without notice and in a matter of no time. Then in that matter of no time, Tomi's shunt again malfunctioned with another blockage (and, as it turned out, a break deep inside his brain) in an event that just happened to coincide with his implant hospitalization. But no one knew at first because there was no deafening awakening like twice before. This event only brought silent slumber. It was odd, though, that Tomi hadn't yet come around from the anesthesia, well after the surgery, and when we *were* able to stir him awake, he vomited (both of which were attributed to the anaphylaxis, at first). But when those eyes started swelling, we knew it! Then a CT scan confirmed it. By that time, a neurosurgeon was ready, and two surgeries later, Tomi's shunt was refitted, and the clock was reset until the next malfunction.

So given all these things and untold others, where's the "recovery" in Tomi's recovery? If recovery is about a return to a normal state of mental or physical health, then is it enough that Tomi is fairly stable at home now, with critical systems functioning within expected limits…that it's become a little easier to breathe…and that those pureed sweet potatoes have all but faded from memory? Is it hopeful that raw sound can now be piped directly into Tomi's brain or that his eyes have stabilized and usually gaze in the same general direction? Is it productive that Tomi's connectedness with things begins with a little YumYum but ends at the limit of an accidental kick? Is it okay that a sweet smile is only one quick seizure away or that Tomi can sometimes be reached in space—if only face-to-face?

Do these things make a recovery?

Practically speaking, it can't ever be enough given the depth and breadth of Tomi's losses, when measured against a typical definition of *recovery*. There isn't a lot of hope for auditory and visual inputs into such neuro-logically devastated space, for *this* isn't really hearing and seeing. And even though a little YumYum soothes and comforts, the world beyond is a much farther, if not impossible, reach. Or a smile for a seizure...this *is not* a good trade, and it's never okay for a child to be so lost that a parent's reach can barely bridge the space—even when face-to-face.

But speaking from the heart, recovery is what we call *this* even though it's life-long and ever-changing, for this is recovery in Tomi's time. We call it recovery because it's not decline—or worse—and because there *is* simply no other name for it. And even though *all* the gains are as modest as maintaining stability and comfort and nurturing what little bit remains, these too are parts of Tomi's recovery. From them, we look back to see that a little healing has occurred for all of us. And because of this, *we have* found it possible to rejoice at Tomi's return to life. We still hope for possibilities. And we can delight in Tomi's progress in ways never before possible.

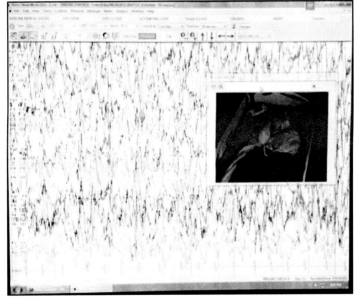

An EEG's View of Chaos in Space

Recovery of a Family

Paling by comparison to all that Tomi has been through, our recovery might simply be a byline in Tomi's time if not for that bond between parent and baby, ever so helpless and utterly dependent. Borne of flesh and blood and nurtured mind and soul, this bond may never be stronger than at birth and through infancy and the like. It's that connection with baby through which pain in the same spreads body part by part and where hardship, bore hand-in-hand and face-to-face, is the only way forward—regardless of the pain. It's that lifeline with him in which death and loss cut by double-edge through the tenderest bits, leaving behind scars that bind us in ways not otherwise possible. It's this bond with Tomi, borne at the end of all things perfect and branded through mind and soul, that both necessitates and at the same time makes possible our recovery.

A simple answer belies such a logical dilemma, though—this ability to heal by the one from whom the need originated. It's one thing for us that makes forward progress possible in the face of overwhelming loss—of the son we were to have, our ways of living and working, our connectedness as wife and husband, our plans and hopes for the future. This one thing is "perspective." But for all the simplicity in this one earthly answer, nothing may be more difficult than maintaining perspective on such a shifting target as Tomi's recovery—particularly since we, ourselves, are sometimes moving objects in the same.

Perspective begins for us with any number of the simplest, most mundane things that parents get to do for their babies in some form or fashion. In the overall context of Tomi's condition, though, most of these things in-and-of themselves may be of marginal benefit. But after combining and making routine, day-after-day, we look back to find a quiet, unseen ground swell beneath our feet that roots us parents and that makes possible everything else that follows...

A day begins with a seizure and then an awakening of a most perfect and beautiful form; a yawn, a stretch, and the sweetest squeaks and coos that remind every time a little boy still exists below the surface.

Then a back and body rub to satisfy the itchy places, ease the stresses of immobility, and to help us reconnect after a long night alone; a bit of personal care to follow: a shower, a fresh diaper and change of clothes, a little teeth brushing, an occasional in-house haircut, for nothing more than our pride in Tomi and for the sake of his humanity.

Some TV time sometimes follows—*Sesame Street*, *Thomas and Friends*, an animated Sweet Pea immersed in all the colorful sights and sounds—not to pawn Tomi off on the television but for hope of stimulating his senses, when it's just not possible to be physically connected with him.

And on with some medical business: tummy-tube cleaning, prep and delivery of the seizure meds and the seizure formula (which doubles as complete nutrition), hooking up the feeding pump and managing it continuously—not that it all makes possible much less than ten per day but to prevent those days of twenty-five or more where rolling seizures and their aftereffects consume every hour of the day.

Then other medical business on a periodic basis, such as appointments with Tomi's pediatrician, the two neurologists and the neurosurgeon, a gastroenterologist, the ophthalmologist and otolaryngologist, and more recently an orthopedic surgeon and pulmonologist, not to mention the occasional physiatrist, neuropsychologist, and the special dentist; and return visits to Children's Hospital for sleep and swallowing studies, replacement of Tomi's G-J tube which regularly pops out, twenty-four-hour videotaped EEGs, an occasional CT scan for fear of the devil's return, and untold other surgeries and emergency room visits for various head and gut problems—all in a desperate struggle at times to maintain Tomi's stability and comfort and to try and figure out some way around his unsolvable problems.

There's also therapy and education in a day including in-home sessions with physical and occupational therapists, occasional visits to clinical therapists of the same plus one for speech, not forgetting visits to the audiologist as well; public school teachers of the most excellent sort; visits to and by The Center for the Visually Impaired, Georgia Sensory Assistance Project, the occasional workshop for the deafblind, and also Ms. Jacque, who is nothing short of Tomi's very own "Anne Sullivan" *and one of the finest human beings we have ever known*; and there's our own therapy and education for Tomi that mirror those of the professionals to the extent possible—but which, more than anything else, nurtures the little bit that remains and seeks to touch him with love so strong that it can't be muted, overlooked, or *unfelt*.

Time also for other important things, not the least of which include dealings with the insurance company and its approved group of middlemen and providers of services, durable medical equipment, and disposable supplies; runarounds with Medicaid, the local DFACS office, and the Department of Public Health (excepting certain special individuals at each); process and dispatch of home health care nurses in *and then out* of our lives because we can better care for Tomi by ourselves (with a little help from a very special family member); having to work weekends and other odd hours because we do care for him ourselves; then trying to make a little fun together: sometimes lunch in the afternoon, a date from time to time, or an occasional vacation somewhere nearby; and lastly, making time for *Tomi's Time* to tell our baby's story in a way that he will never know but that will hopefully speak to families who now find themselves on a similar road, sharing a similar perspective.

And at the end of a day, after working in the grocery shopping, cooking, bill paying, housework, cat box cleaning, laundry, and whatever else comprises the daily business of living, one last seizure and then time for the next long night's sleep, usually worn-down and sometimes beaten down, but not without gain or fulfillment—not without love and having had the chance to be parents for a day.

This is a perspective that moves us forward. But claiming this is what it's *all* about would render Tomi's story unworthy of telling. So with humility and hope for forgiveness, a different perspective in a way—or alternate reality—where diminished gains and exhumed fulfillment pull back on forward progress and where we sometimes find ourselves recoiling in the face of pain and hardship...

A day begins with a seizure and the sounds of screeching and straining as limbs go rigid and face wrenches into contortion; or sometimes, it's the sound of vomit and the ever-present danger it's being aspirated or that it's signaling the next shunt malfunction; other times, it's a bottom burst: pajamas, sheets, and crib covered in it with his YumYum dreadfully unsoiled—all, never ceasing to remind that our baby will *never* grow up.

Straight then to the shower with no time to touch or reconnect, only urgency and desperation and that intensifying screaming from being blasted through space; shower running, clothes off, never mind the perfect temperature and delivery method—only *urgency and desperation* as the shower streams pierce that tender flesh.

Then a crescendo of screaming and flailing, followed by sensory overload and system shutdown: a seizure of a different sort with head twisted to extreme, eyes turned to space, still and silent (for a time); quick, then, to throw on a diaper and some clothes, and then a little mouth washing because things are strangely easier during and after any seizure event—but it's *never easy* starting the day this way, with pride buried in pain and hardship and recurring questions about the humanity of it all.

What's the point, then, to TV time or hanging out in each other's face or holding hands, after a seizure knockout and the usual spacing and sleeping that follow (excepting a few brief moments of clarity that follow each)—at which point, nothing more to do but set up in the safest and most comfortable planter possible and choke on the utter disconnect and abandonment that comes with it.

But still on with the medical business, delivering the usual treatments despite the nominal difference between ten and twenty-five per day; then an awakening from the previous event, only to begin the next some minutes later (maybe five, maybe fifty or so, *or this time, thirteen, just during the time it's taken to write this sentence about it*). So goes an absolutely desperate cycle that's perpetuated by waking, from which the only difference between ten and twenty-five is how few precious minutes of clarity pass after each return.

And the pediatrician and those eleven specialists (with, no doubt, body parts for more), that forgotten count of surgeries, procedures, and studies (that still count), and wonder at how life managed to prevail, particularly through those first couple years and even today, for there is no solution or cure for the problem or even a way around it. Sometimes it's only a matter of holding on for dear life and occasionally wondering if things would have been better otherwise.

All this calling to question the outcomes possible through therapy and education: developmental ability seemingly obliterated before development ever really progressed; the degree of encephalopathy requiring two neurologists and a neurosurgeon; that silent darkness, unbreechable by any lens or device the ophthalmologist may have or the cochlear implant from that world-renowned otolaryngologist (who nearly met his match installing it); setting aside the physiatrist and neuropsychologist who have nothing more to add at this point, as well as the other specialists whose interests are in other pieces and parts—because it's really *all* about the brain and the space that lies within.

And still more questions and hope lost when hearing, "I am *so* sorry, but we just don't have the resources here to help," this from the administrator of a private school for disabled kids, tears in her eyes, understanding in ours, and others returning to space; and previous thoughts of The Perkins School in Boston, however many miles away from everyone and everything we have here, however none better for this kind of problem, but in the end, risks and costs seemingly outweigh the likely benefits, particularly since the need is more basic than all that: when clinging upon whatever remains and straining for hope that even love will ever get through.

With all this, not much to say about other daily business like careers and insurance dealings, given what they provide and all they mean—simply "necessary" drains on precious, waning time that could otherwise be spent holding hands.

But Medicaid is a different deal altogether, when it takes three seizures and a vomiting spell to get through the welfare office for the annual qualifications renewal, not that qualifying conditions will ever change, but in spite of them because it's impossible to ever say that we're grateful to be there. Then there's the privileged need of standing in a line in which we have no business being, not that people don't need a little help along the way, and not that we can't stand with them either way, but that certain needs sometimes justify their own lines and their own set of rules. And when the rules, such that they are, get fouled by the ones paid to administer them and then that's followed with self-righteous indignation and a demand that we "Must Wait And Come Back Another Day," then the hell that pours forth from *this* head is unmistakably evil and obvious to all—even to our own with sound, sight, and father (even more so) removed.

But other times, it's wife and husband removed, even bound to our own and pulling in the same direction, love and empathy for each other well-intact, hoping and sharing for better; but things change when the unthinkable happens to a child, the kind of things that alter personalities and that shift priorities and perspectives, things that can take away all the fun in marriage and that sometimes render spouses into roommates who happen to share a single, common cause.

Even yet, time still spent finishing this story; at times like these, not that it will change a thing for subject or audience, alike—but for us (*and much more for me*), to never forget the best and worst parts of it all and as a guide to better parenthood in this uncertain future.

And at the end of a day, after setting aside the grocery shopping, cooking, bill paying, housework, cat-box cleaning, laundry, and whatever else comprises the daily business of decline, one last seizure and then time for the next long night's sleep, usually beaten down and sometimes broken, gain and fulfillment a little bit in question—but still, not without love and having had survived another day of parenthood.

Tom Zarzaca

A nondescript line sometimes exists between these two perspectives, both of which play out on a daily basis to varying degrees, but at the end of the day, the only real difference being the rate at which we're able to move forward.

If any line is to be drawn between the two, however, it would have to be tied to the degree of urgency in Tomi's condition at any given time and to a recurring sense of desperation that sometimes comes with it. But as each return event and time have come to pass, this sense has eased a bit, at first by a numbness that set in from the intense and prolonged emotional trauma of that first year or so, then by a kind of unwilling submission to the unreal reality of it all, and later, even acceptance that this reality is only "Life" playing out along one of many possible roads:

Similar to some roads of parents whose child is born with profound disabilities, maybe unknowing of another way to parent their baby and accepting of the hand that was given to them; or similar in other ways to parents with child and terminal illness, who know an end is coming (or already passed) and who let go when time to release the hand dealt to them; or even yet, similar to some parents who face the loss of a child to a freak accident, a debilitating cognitive or emotional disorder, or

50

maybe even institutionalization, who are powerless to change the past but who know they just can't stop.

So there's no doubt that if any of us are to recover, then the healing must begin with Yuko and me—and our ability to accept this utter change, to let go of the loss (but never Tomi), and to continue forward despite whatever uncertainty the future may hold.

We also share another double-sided perspective that's rooted in a different reality and time altogether—that first nine months of Tomi's life, when pure delight carried the day from beginning to end. While this perspective backdrops the change that's occurred and can sometimes gorge a recurring sense of loss, it also sustains our bond to Tomi that reaches all the way back to his first breath:

Emerging then and now again, in new life, a most extraordinary and beautiful little creature who was—and still is—our son and who will always be our baby; entering this world then as now, without sense of the Life around him but with us, still, helping him into it; and completely dependent getting there, never more than the present, save the future perhaps, but carried through since that first day by our love for Tomi and an infantile devotion that just can't be released or outgrown at this point; for such fragility and vulnerability beg undivided attention and constant protection because the unthinkable was—and still may be—waiting just down the road (as may be other unimaginable things); whereupon now, we look back to see it's been the same road all along, only differently directed by way of an end that met new life— and now, *a Beginning in which we have too much to lose and so much to gain.*

Because this perspective focuses on what we have—and not all that's been lost or how far we will always have to go—we focus on Tomi (and not us), amazed at the beauty of our child, so pure, and a love for him like we never before imagined.

In this way, Tomi himself heals us. He is our way forward, whereby doing for him, face-to-face, frees us from our own chaotic blast through space and recovery and brings us into the relative comfort and stillness of Tomi's unique time.

Morning Sun at Four Years

A Pretty Good Trade

An Uncertain Future

An uncertain future…it begins in the past in some way with a decision or two—maybe even a lifetime of decisions. An uncertain future is always there, and it carries with it any number of potential outcomes. Just ask a quantum physicist about it. They say it's not possible to predict the condition of a particle—an atom, a living cell, a human being—at any point in the future, as if life is shaped by random chance and driven on by decisions made and decisions un-made. However, Einstein's perspective wasn't in the quantum world. It was all about relativity for him, and he hated the thought of God rolling dice (as he put it). From Einstein's deterministic view, things work out as they should according to certain fundamental laws and a beautiful, exquisitely mastered plan.

But like most things in life, reality probably exists somewhere between the two (and at the same time, it is the two), and it's much more complicated than a scientist can comprehend and far simpler than any one religion can explain. But for a baby who has lost nearly everything—and for us who love and care for Tomi—an uncertain future holds a very unique, yet paradoxical meaning.

Tom Zarzaca

A Paradox—

So what of *our* uncertain future?

On the surface, the uncertainty of our future may seem far less than that of a typical family, in which a child grows up, goes to college somewhere, gets married and has a number of kids, works a career of unknown possibilities, and gracefully matures into old age. Because of Tomi's losses, the possibility of these major life events happening for him is as remote as any star in space, and the number of potential outcomes in his life is therefore many fewer— making things a little more "certain" for him. And just as Tomi will never go to college, neither will he be a high school dropout, in trouble with the law, strung out on drugs, or worse. Tomi will never marry, but at the same time, his heart will never be broken by loss of love, and he'll never know the pain and hardship that can follow the loss of a child or the sorrow that comes at the end of all things perfect. All these potential outcomes in a life, wiped clean from the list of possibilities for Tomi, *seemingly* making things more certain for all of us.

Instead, the uncertainty of our future begins below the surface with an overwhelming question at the end: *What happens to Tomi when we're gone?* And other, more specific questions that, in part, define the last: What gains are possible over the course of Tomi's life, when it really is all about maintaining stability and comfort and nurturing the little bit that remains? What can be done to protect Tomi from would-be predators whose undetected approach could come from anywhere, at any time? How will we provide for Tomi, now that he is our new career, in which the only meaningful enrichment is Tomi, himself? Who will be there to embrace him on his hundred-thousandth seizure, or will it only be his silent darkness? These are a few questions that speak of our uncertain future. Others remain, and without doubt, more will follow down the road...

But as we move farther *back* in time, more toward the present, questions and answers of an uncertain future gradually come into focus. Things become a little clearer with time's regression, and paradox thereby unfolds.

We hope, for instance, that all we do for Tomi sets an example for whomever follows in our footsteps and that, just maybe, they will love him as their own. *We believe* that we're reaching Tomi and hope that this one amazingly beautiful outcome will one day be felt as love—and perhaps even remembered in some way when we're gone. *We think* we can keep Tomi medically stable in the months and years to come and that, while we were busy talking to our baby and holding on to him for dear life, the worst bit already passed by. *We understand* that life will go on tomorrow in some way, but that today, it does so with a little more clarity—and in a manner that we choose and in Tomi's time that we now keep. *We have faith* that we belong on the road that we travel—for reasons still unknown, still unrevealed. Whether this road simply follows from decisions made and decisions un-made or whether it's a tiny part of that exquisite plan—or both—*we know* we were made for our baby and that our love for him grows by the day. *And at this very moment, as this part of Tomi's time draws to a close, nothing else in the universe could be more certain than this.*

Beginning

This beginning for us—"in all its different forms, with all its different meanings, and for all the change it brings…"—continues, now, four years after Tomi's recovery began. When first putting these words to our beginning, they may have been little more than a desperate attempt to understand what was happening to Tomi and to come to terms with what the future could possibly hold for us. These beginning words were also a humbled reach for hope of a father, speaking for family—trying to piece together some imagined way forward with then-vacant steps that could only to be taken later, if perspective and time permitted.

Some of these steps, now footprints in a line that extends just underfoot, show us one way forward. This way isn't revealed to us by looking ahead, though. For we've already witnessed the unthinkable and discovered some things unimaginable, and we now know that any number of them can happen again in the future.

Tom Zarzaca

Instead, our way forward is rooted in the past, among the basest forms of a beginning, when an end met new life and Tomi's rebirth began:

> Starting as a baby *without form*—still and silent, little distinction between life and death, and each then staking their claim on things; then a return to life only to be devoured by a *darker form*—a living hell that comes and goes, leaving nothing behind but its deafening promise to return again; all the while, a *life form lost*—a shell of a little boy who animates like he did when he first came to being and who scarcely comprehends who he is and what place he holds in time.

> But at the heart of it all is the *form of our baby, reborn*— a pure infant child, permanently removed from the corrupting sights, sounds, and desires of the material world and free to ascend beyond in his own unique way; a *Pure Form of freedom*—for a human being, unbound by chains of the mind who delivers us from our own and who teaches us a truer, more lasting meaning of enrichment; and so shines a *form of Pure Light*—who guides us to turn from our own shadows and embrace the light behind, as no one less than the sun himself.

From this past, our way forward is made possible in the present, for this is the only place in Tomi's time where the paradox can exist. It's the only way we can understand and accept, with some certainty, *some* of the meaning behind all that has happened to Tomi—that his loss of sense, the return events, and a smile that went missing seemingly ages ago and many decisions since—means that the child we had is lost to another reality and time altogether. But at the same time, we gained a son of such exquisite purity and innocence that we can't let go of him, and loving him is all that's left to do...What it means to us, loving Tomi in this way after he almost lost the ability to respond to it, is that we share a love for him like we *never* before imagined and would not have otherwise known.

And in the context of all the change that took place since Tomi's very first day, *this* love means that very little changes today except deepening bonds, less conditioned along the way. In this way, our Beginning is becoming a way of life as we carry along the road to whatever future we make together and however long Tomi's time takes us to get there.

And with Tomi's story now complete through the present, it's time to set it aside for later reading—and later writing, when the time is right. There's more to be said of our journey so far and we hope much more to come in delivering our lifelong promise to Tomi.

Companion, Still. . .

Please visit

www.ReachingTomi.com

to follow Tomi's continued progress.

About the Author

Tom Zarzaca was born in 1966 in Atlanta, Georgia, a self-described troublemaker and late bloomer who only needed a little direction and purpose in life. During and after high school, he was an artist of sorts and at times a pretty good food service waiter but later became a horrible automobile salesman. And with this modest beginning, the US Navy was the only thing left to do, and he enlisted and proudly served aboard the aircraft carrier USS *Forrestal* during the 1990 Persian Gulf War. Ultimately, he would attend college and graduate cum laude in biological engineering from University of Georgia, where he met and later married Yuko to form a perfect little pair. And over the ten years that followed, he went on to build a career as a registered civil engineer in consultancy, during which time Tomi was born; the pair became three—in one— and his purpose in life was finally revealed.